SUGAR AND SPICE

The ABC of Being a Girl

VERSES BY *Phyllis McGinley*

PICTURES BY *Colleen Browning*

Franklin Watts, Inc.
575 LEXINGTON AVENUE, NEW YORK 22

Library of Congress Catalog Card Number: 60-11203

TEXT © COPYRIGHT 1959, 1960 BY PHYLLIS McGINLEY
ILLUSTRATIONS © COPYRIGHT 1960 BY FRANKLIN WATTS, INC.
Manufactured in the United States of America

*

COMPOSED BY *Westcott & Thomson, Inc.*, Philadelphia
PRINTED BY *Polygraphic Company of America, Inc.*, New York
BOUND BY *H. Wolff Book Manufacturing Company, Inc.*, New York

*

DESIGNED BY CHARLES FARRELL

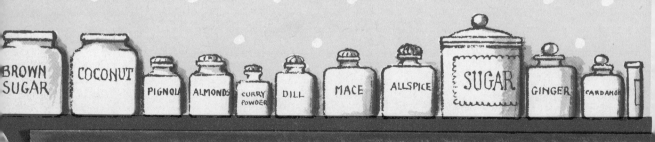

SUGAR AND SPICE

Often at night
When the dark slips free,
I think how I might have been born
Not Me.
I might have been somebody else or other
With a different father and a different mother
And different friends whom I wouldn't enjoy,
Or oh, good gracious,
I might have been a boy!

Then you can't imagine how glad I get
And I count right through the alphabet,
Naming the things from A to Z
That belong to girls
And that make me
Me.

Aprons, for instance.
I do like those,
Mine have pockets
And they tie with bows.
I always wear them
On afternoons
When we're making cookies.
(I lick the spoons.)
Some morning when I
Can spare a minute,
I'll bake a pie
And put apples in it.

B's full of blessings a girl can use
Like books and bracelets and ballet shoes.
There's Betsy, my bride doll, dressed in white,
And the blinking bubbles
In my bath at night.

C

When company comes whom I haven't met,
I always curtsy (if I don't forget).
And I pass the cake and I don't spill crumbs.
I'm careful of my manners
When company comes.

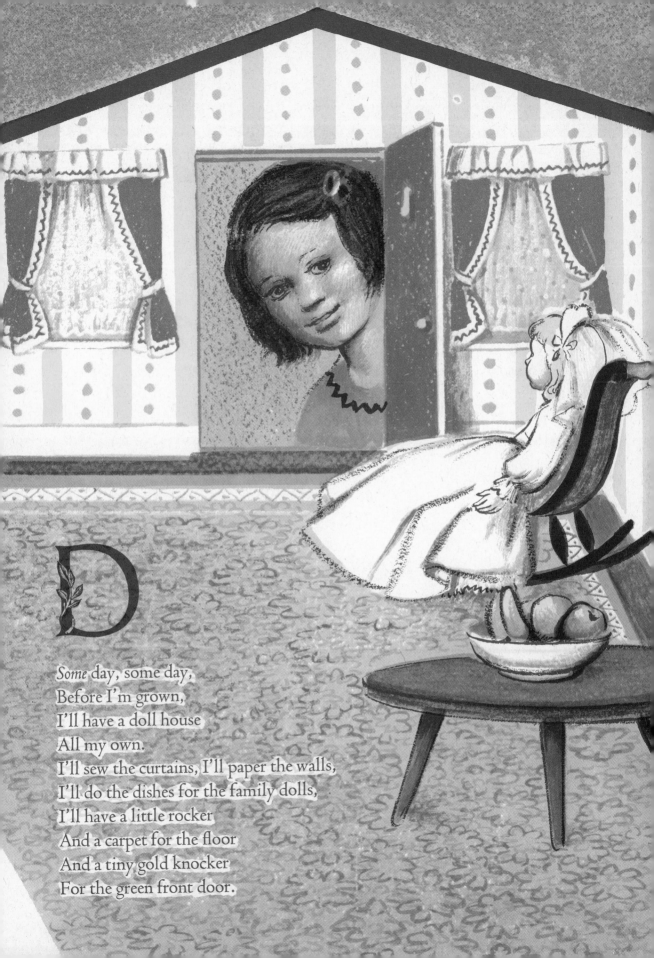

Some day, some day,
Before I'm grown,
I'll have a doll house
All my own.
I'll sew the curtains, I'll paper the walls,
I'll do the dishes for the family dolls,
I'll have a little rocker
And a carpet for the floor
And a tiny gold knocker
For the green front door.

When I am eighteen or a little bit older,
I'm going to wear earrings that hang to my shoulder.
I'll feel like an empress, I'll walk like a queen,
In high heels and earrings, when I am eighteen.

F

Felicia Frances is my firm, fast friend.
We have more fun
Playing let's-pretend.
Sometimes we're princesses, sometimes we're spies,
Sometimes we're Indians, feathered to the eyes,
Sometimes we're Eskimos, fastened into furs,
But she's always my friend
And I am hers.

G

G is games like giant steps that everybody loves.
It's gardens full of marigolds. It's my five-fingered gloves.
It's going to the grocery store to get me something sweet.
But G also is gentle things
Like grace before we eat.

H

Have you heard the hoofs of our horses
　　Hammering through the weeds?
We gallop, we fly,
Felicia and I
　　On our highbred hunting steeds.
And it isn't old brooms we're riding
　　As maybe the neighbors say,
But "Devil-may-care," Felicia's mare,
　　And "Happy," my dapple-grey.

I can skate on ice, I can write with ink,
But ironing's what I do best, I think,
When I press the napkins as flat as leaves
Or smooth out my father's
Handkerchiefs.

Just before June
Comes jump-rope time
When everybody skips to a skipping rhyme,
Or sitting on steps with sun at our backs,
Everybody jumbles everybody's jacks.
While balls are bouncing and jump-ropes twirl,
It's awfully jolly
Being a girl.

K

My kitten's called Katinka.
Bright yellow are her eyes.
She tangles mother's knitting,
She chases butterflies
With leaps so high and mighty
I almost think it's true
Katinka's partly kitten
And partly kangaroo.

L is the loveliest letter made.
It's lilacs and lockets and lemonade,
It's the lake where I swim in a rubber cap,
And it's laughing out loud,
And my mother's lap.

M

Many people mention I'm the image of my mother.
    Other people murmur that I've got my father's brow.
While grandfather Grover says I'm grandma all over.
    But I honestly don't see how.
For I peer in the mirror
And who do I see?
Me.

N

Nights aren't scary. They're nice and cozy
When my nightgown's on and I'm feeling dozy,
When I've brushed my teeth and said my prayers
And the clock ticks neighborly
From the stairs.

O

Out in a meadow where I often go,
There's a very old oaktree, branching low.
An oriole family, all summer through,
Has a house there. I have one, too.
A green roof glimmers above my head.
Over me, over me, green boughs spread.
I've moss for a tablecloth, roots for a chair,
And only my dolls can visit me there.

P

Felicia is planning a party,
    She's printing us all a note.
I'll wear my pink dress
With the pleating, I guess,
    And my starchiest petticoat.
We'll pin a tail on the donkey
    With blindfolds over our eyes,
While everyone brings
Her presents and things,
    And everyone wins a prize.

My grandmother's grandmother helped to sew
This quilt with its pattern of calico,
Long ago, long ago
When she wasn't much older than I. I keep
Hoping she knows how quiet, how deep,
Under her quilt I sleep.

R

We're racing, racing down the walk,
Over the pavement and round the block.
We rumble along till the sidewalk ends—
Felicia and I and half our friends.
Our hair flies backward. It's whish and whirr!
She roars at me and I shout at her
As past the porches and garden gates
We rattle and rock
On our roller skates.

S

I love the smell of scenty soap and lavender sachet,
The smell of sheets along the line upon a sunny day,
The salt smell of seashores, the furry smell of pets,
And the talcum smell of babies when they're snug in bassinets.

When I was smaller I wasn't able
To see the top of the dining-room table.
But now I've grown to such a height,
I have my dinner there, every night.
If I wash my hands
And comb my hair,
My father stands
To hold my chair.

u

I don't mind rain (if it doesn't thunder)
For I've an umbrella to shelter under.
I can open it up,
I can shut it down.
I can walk around dry in the rainy town,
Or meet my uncle at the evening bus
And hold my umbrella over us.

V

I'm very fond of a valentine.
I like the sort that says "Please Be Mine";
The velvet hearts that Felicia gives;
The candy ones
From my relatives;
The funny kind
(I know where they're bought at)
That sensible girls can laugh a lot at;
And the made-at-home ones, stuck with glue,
Left at the doorsill and signed
                                        "Guess Who."

W

Have you ever been a witch?
Well, I have—
One worse than you might suppose,
With a mop and a cat and a pointed hat
And a frightening pointed nose.
And I whisked along on the magic street,
Crying my witch song,
"Trick or treat!"

X

The letters I send
To my grandmother end
 With a great big inky X.
The reason for this is
To stand for the kisses
 My grandmother always expects.

Y Our yard is full of lots of things—
Doll carriages
And sand
And swings
And slides and rubber balls and dishes.
I guess my mother often wishes
I wouldn't play there quite so hard,
But that's the reason for
A yard.

Z is a funny one.
Z's for zippers
On coats
And dresses
And bedroom slippers.
Z is for zinnias blazing in the sun.
Z's for the zoo
Where the zebras run.
(Wouldn't it be lovely
To have one for a pet?)
And Z is the end of my
Alphabet.

Yes, often at night
When the shadows swirl,
I think how it's pleasant to be a girl.
Then I name my letters and run them through
For things that I'm glad about.
Why don't you?

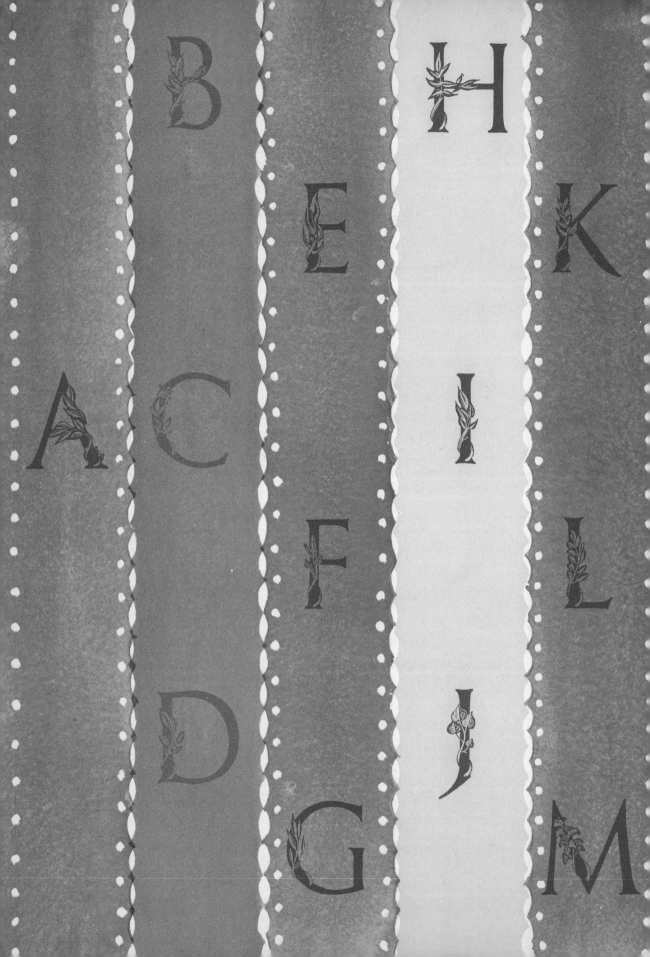